perfect your pronouns

Pronouns are useful because they can be used instead of repeating a noun.

Replace the nouns (underlined below) with personal pronouns from the box.

1. The reds beat the blues. **The reds** won by two points. _____

2. Jack loved the film when **Jack** saw **the film**. _____

3. Bella is in my class. Do you know **Bella**? _____

4. Our neighbours are friendly when you get to know **our neighbours**. _____

Personal pronouns:

I	they / them
we / us	it
you	he / she
him/her	

Possessive pronouns tell you who owns something, eg The bike belongs to Tom. It's **his**.

Choose possessive pronouns to complete the following sentences:

1. The ice cream belongs to Amy. It's _____ .

2. The snake belongs to us. It's _____ .

3. The hat belongs to you. It's _____ .

4. The car belongs to them. It's _____ .

Possessive pronouns:

mine / ours	theirs
his / hers	its
yours	

stick a reward sticker here!

adding adjectives

An **adjective** is a describing word that tells you more about a noun.

For example, a building… a **new** building… a **wonderful, new** building

Underline the adjectives in the sentences below.

1. The clever detective caught the notorious thief.

2. Spectacular fireworks lit up the dark sky.

3. A big, hairy spider sat beside the little boy.

get it?

Adding adjectives before the noun will make your writing more interesting and informative for the reader.

Add adjectives before the nouns in these sentences. Write on the lines below.

1. The dog chased the cat.

_____

2. We had a meal in a restaurant.

_____

3. She wore a dress and shoes.

_____

_____

stick a reward sticker here!

4

comparing adjectives

Compare these adjectives. The first one has been done for you.

	er	est
small	smaller	smallest
big	_____	_____
loud	_____	_____
funny	_____	_____
healthy	_____	_____

Sometimes we make a comparison by using **more**, **less** or **most** before an adjective.

less beautiful	more beautiful	most beautiful
less efficient	more efficient	most efficient

Underline the comparative adjectives in these sentences.

1. The triceratops was heavier than two elephants.

2. Energy-saving bulbs last longer than ordinary bulbs.

3. Wind energy is greener than oil.

4. Vegetables are healthier than cakes.

5. Of all the jellyfish, the box jellyfish is the most deadly.

5

verbs and adverbs

A **verb** is a doing word. It tells us about the action taking place.

Which of these sentences sounds the most interesting?

WEAK VERB

1. The boy **went** across the field.

BETTER VERB

2. The boy **ran** across the field.

VERB + ADVERB

3. The boy **ran quickly** across the field.

POWERFUL VERB

4. The boy **sprinted** across the field.

get it?

The sentence with the powerful verb is the most interesting. It is better to use one powerful word rather than lots of weaker ones.

Think of more powerful verbs to replace those underlined below.

1. The car <u>went</u> down the road. _____

2. The mouse <u>went</u> under the sofa. _____

3. The waves <u>went</u> onto the rocks. _____

4. The girl <u>went</u> down the corridor. _____

5. The boy <u>went</u> into the cave. _____

An **adverb** will tell us more about a verb.

Write an adverb after these verbs. Choose from the box or use your own.

1. He looked _____ at his opponent.

2. They spoke _____ on the phone.

3. She sang _____ into the microphone.

4. The wind blew _____ .

5. The volcano erupted _____ .

Adverbs:

fiercely	quietly
angrily	jokingly
softly	violently
kindly	loudly
suddenly	gently

get it?

An adverb can change the meaning of the verb. For example, someone can look **suspiciously** or look **curiously** around a room.

stick a
reward
sticker
here!

playing with words

Similes are when you describe something as being <u>like</u> something else.

For example, the rocks were jagged **like shark's teeth**.

Make up some of your own similes to complete these descriptions:

1. The crashing waves were like _____

2. The hot sun was like _____

3. The autumn leaves were like _____

4. The tiger's eyes were like _____

Metaphors are when you say that something <u>is</u> something else.

For example, She's a clown! (She is someone who is always joking.)

Choose a metaphor to describe these people or things.

1. someone who is always smiling _____

2. someone who is sneaky _____

3. a tiny flaw that spoils something _____

4. someone who stays up late _____

Metaphors:

a snake in the grass   a ray of sunshine

a fly in the ointment   a night owl

Proverbs are common sayings or comments about life.

Write what you think these proverbs mean:

1. The grass is always greener on the other side.

_____

2. Don't put all your eggs in one basket.

_____

3. Two heads are better than one.

_____

4. Better late than never!

_____

5. All that glitters is not gold.

_____

Onomatopoeia is a word that sounds like the thing it is describing.

BUZZ!   CRASH!   POP!   GLUG!   SQUELCH!   PLOP!   SQUEAK!

Write some more examples of onomatopoeia:

_____

Palindromes are words that read the same backwards and forwards.

For example, Anna, mum, dad.

Write some more palindromes:

I KNOW A PALINDROME: D-I-D

_____

full stops and capitals

We put **full stops** (.) in sentences in places where we would pause when reading the words.

Read the following passage and add full stops where you think the pauses should be.

i wake up each morning before the alarm i wait for it to ring on the dot of seven and then i get up but today was going to be different i didn't wake up the alarm didn't ring this difference would change my life forever

Go back to the same passage above and add capital letters for 'I', and for the start of each sentence.

Now check against the following text:

I wake up each morning before the alarm. I wait for it to ring on the dot of seven and then I get up. But today was going to be different. I didn't wake up. The alarm didn't ring. This difference would change my life forever.

How did you score? Give yourself one point for each correct full stop and capital letter.

my score _____

semicolons and colons

A **semicolon** (;) joins parts of a sentence where there are closely connected ideas.

For example:

I didn't wake up; the alarm didn't ring.

get it?

When reading aloud, the pause for a semicolon is not as long as the pause for a full stop.

Write a sentence that contains a semicolon. Use it to link your ideas together.

_____

Colons (:) appear at the start of a list or just before an idea.

For example:

To make my favourite sandwich you will need: bread, margarine, tuna and cucumber.

If you are writing a complicated list, you can use semicolons to help you separate the items.

For example:

To make my favourite sandwich, you will need: wholemeal or brown bread, cut into two slices; thinly-sliced cucumber; drained tuna flakes; and reduced-fat, low-salt margarine.

Write a list of ingredients (starting with a colon) for your favourite sandwich. Add commas and/or semicolons to separate items in the list.

For my favourite sandwich, you will need

_____

11

how to use apostrophes

Apostrophes have two important jobs:

1. An apostrophe tells you who owns what – this is called **possession**. For example, the shark's teeth (the teeth belonging to the shark).

2. An apostrophe tells you which words are shortened – this is called **contraction**. For example, It's a shark! (It is a shark!).

Write a phrase containing a possessive apostrophe for each of the statements below.

The first one has been done for you.

1. the desk belonging to the teacher   the teacher's desk

2. the purse belonging to Mum

3. the studio belonging to the artist

4. the whiskers belonging to the cat

Now check out the 'get it' at the top of the next page before you do the questions below.

Write a phrase containing a plural possessive apostrophe for the statements below.

The first one has been done for you.

1. the dog belonging to the girls   the girls' dog

2. the car belonging to the family

3. the changing room belonging to the players

4. the jobs belonging to the people

5. the toys belonging to the babies

HELP! I CAN'T SWIM!

Apostrophes are also used when you want to shorten words or phrases. The apostrophe replaces the missing letters.

Learn these contractions:

I am – **I'm**
he is / she is – **he's / she's**
it is – **it's**
you are – **you're**
they are – **they're**
we are – **we're**

do not – **don't**
did not – **didn't**
does not – **doesn't**
cannot – **can't**
could not – **couldn't**
would not – **wouldn't**

Use an apostrophe to shorten words in each of the sentences below.

The first one has been done for you.

1. We cannot go yet.   We can't go yet.

2. She did not like the taste.

3. The dog does not bite.

4. The car will not start.

5. It is not fair!

HOW DO YOU STOP A DOG FROM SMELLING?

HOLD ITS NOSE! (NOT: IT'S NOSE!)

13

speech!

stick a reward sticker here!

Speech marks (" ") tell you exactly what words are spoken by the characters in a story.

get it?

Speech marks are drawn at the beginning (") and at the end (") of the spoken words. All other punctuation goes inside of them.

Read the story extract and draw speech marks around the words that are said by the characters.

I think Dig is sick, said Tom. He won't eat his dinner.

Perhaps he's not hungry, replied Tom's mum.

But he's *always* hungry! said Tom. And it's his favourite: marinated chicken chunks in juicy jelly.

Continue the conversation between Tom and his mum on the lines below. Start a new line for each new speaker. Draw speech marks around the words that are spoken.

HE'S JUST ATTENTION-SEEKING!

Conversation often has question marks or exclamation marks.

Question marks (?) tell you that a question is being asked.

Exclamation marks (!) show surprise, humour or excitement.

Read the story extract. Change the punctuation by substituting question marks or exclamation marks where you think they belong.

"Mum," shouted Tom.

"Now what," said Tom's mum.

"I know why Dig won't eat his dinner," said Tom. "It's a new recipe. They've added vegetables. You know he hates vegetables."

Continue the conversation between Tom and his mum on the lines below. Include speech marks, question marks and exclamation marks where necessary.

_____

_____

_____

_____

_____

_____

_____

AW, DIDDUMS WON'T EAT HIS VEGETABLES!

clauses and conjunctions

A sentence or a clause has to include a noun and a verb.

For example:
Dig loves chicken.

Dig is a noun and **loves** is a verb.

A **conjunction** is a connecting word (sometimes called a connective) that links clauses or sentences.

Conjunctions:	
and	or
but	because
so	when
if	while

For example:
Dig loves chicken. He hates vegetables.
Dig loves chicken **but** he hates vegetables.

Use a conjunction to write one sentence each time.

1. Dig didn't eat his dinner. Kit ate it instead.

_____

2. Dig and Kit were friends. They were rivals too.

_____

3. Tom was worried. Dig didn't eat.

_____

4. Mum wasn't paying attention. She was busy.

_____

Write a sentence of your own using a conjunction.

_____

wow!

oops!

fab!

oh, no!

cool!

easy peasy!

nooo!

yes!!

woo!

oops!

wow!

yay!

brill!

lol

score!

woo!

yay!

yikes!

ok!

gr8!

yippee!

not bad!

great!

wicked!

cool!

ok!

brill!

fab!

cool! ok! brill! fab!

yippee! not bad! great! wicked!

yay! yikes! ok! gr8!

wow! oops! fab! oh, no!

cool! easy peasy! nooo! yes!!

woo! oops! wow! yay!

brill! lol score! woo!

Underline the conjunctions in these sentences.

1. I put the dog on the lead **and** we went out for a walk.

2. It felt cold **although** it was sunny.

3. We played in the park **until** it was dark.

4. Mum was cross **when** I got home late.

5. I missed my programme **because** it came on earlier than usual.

Write another sentence of your own using a conjunction.

_____

Sometimes we use **adverbs** to connect sentences and paragraphs so that our writing 'flows' better.

For example:
We were watching TV. Suddenly, all the lights went out.

Underline the adverbs that connect these sentences.

1. I missed the last five minutes of the film. Consequently, I don't know how it ended!

2. I can come to your house. However, I can't stay for long.

3. Firstly, you mix the butter and the sugar. Next, you add the egg.

4. Dad did the shopping. Meanwhile, Mum was at work.

5. Do your homework now. Later, you can go swimming.

Some connecting adverbs:

later

suddenly

finally

firstly

next

however

meanwhile

consequently

Write two sentences of your own and connect them using an adverb.

_____

_____

_____

_____

get it?

However is a connecting adverb.

17

prefix

A **prefix** is a group of letters at the beginning of a word.

For example:
preschool
prehistoric

The prefix 'pre' means 'before' (in Latin).

Add prefixes to these words.

1. 'aqua' (means 'water' in Latin)

_ _ _ _ _rium

_ _ _ _ _tic

_ _ _ _ _marine

2. 'viv' (means 'live' in Latin)

_ _ _isect

_ _ _ _acious

_ _ _id

3. 'geo' (means 'Earth' in Greek)

_ _ _metry

_ _ _logy

_ _ _graphy

4. 'bio' (means 'life' in Greek)

_ _ _graphy

_ _ _nic

_ _ _ _logical

5. 'oct' (means 'eight' in Greek)

_ _ _opus

_ _ _agon

_ _ _ave

6. 'super' (means 'over' or 'above' in Latin)

_ _ _ _ _ _market

_ _ _ _ _ _sonic

_ _ _ _ _ _store

suffix

A **suffix** is a group of letters at the end of a word.

Using a suffix can change the tense (from past to present tense and vice versa) or the meaning of a word.

Suffixes:

-en / -ed	-ish	-ation	-less	-ment
-er / -or	-ing	-ful	-ly	-ness

Add suffixes to these words.

1. instruct + or = _____

2. act + or = _____

3. conduct + or = _____

4. hope + less = _____

5. sleep + less = _____

6. rest + less = _____

7. excite + ment = _____

8. move + ment = _____

9. agree + ment = _____

10. immediate + ly = _____

11. sudden + ly = _____

12. extreme + ly = _____

When the root word ends in a vowel and you want to add a suffix that starts with a vowel, you drop one of the vowels.

Try these:

1. spice + ed = _____

2. care + ing = _____

3. late + er = _____

Double the consonant when there is a single vowel before a single consonant, eg sit + ing = sitting.

Try these:

4. big + est = _____

5. swim + ing = _____

6. stop + ed = _____

Learn these:
beauty + ful = beautiful
happy + ness = happiness

get it?

The vowels are: **a, e, i, o, u.** The other letters in the alphabet are called consonants.

plural suffixes

stick a reward sticker here!

Sometimes you just add an **s** to make a word plural (more than one). Other times you add **es**. How do you know when to add **s** or **es**?

If a word ends in **ch**, **sh**, **s**, **ss** or **x** you usually add **es**.

Try these:

wish _____

kiss _____

box _____

lunch _____

bus _____

If a word ends in a consonant before a **y**, we drop the **y** and add **ies**.

Try these:

city _____

pony _____

memory _____

dictionary _____

Some words don't follow the rules!

You just have to learn them:

mouse – mice

child – children

man – men

woman – women

deer – deer

potato – potatoes

volcano – volcanoes

video – videos

rhymes and alliteration

stick a reward sticker here!

The way a word begins and ends is important when writing poetry.

Words that begin with the same sounds are called **alliterations**.

Words that end with the same sounds are called **rhymes**.

Read the poem:

> My dog Dig,
> Chomps our shoes,
> Chases the cat
> And eats the news!

1. Which two words rhyme in the poem? _____

2. Which words begin with the same sounds? _____

3. Write a list of words that rhyme with '**shoes**'.

_____

4. Choose one of these words to write an alternative last line.

_____

5. Write a short poem about an animal or a person that includes alliteration and rhyme.

_____

_____

_____

_____

different kinds of writing

stick a reward sticker here!

Diaries, letters, recounts and autobiographies are written in the **first person** using the pronouns I, my, mine and we.

Underline the first-person pronouns in this diary extract:

Somehow I knew that today was going to be special, even though it started off like every other day – I was going to be late for school again!

Instructions and advertisements are written in the **second person** using the pronouns you and your.

Underline the second-person pronouns in this instruction text:

To make chocolate brownies you need: flour, cocoa powder, eggs, butter and milk. But first, you need to find an adult or parent to help you!

Novels, stories, information books and newspaper reports are written in the **third person** using the pronouns he, she, it and they.

Underline the third-person pronouns in this story extract:

"I'm so happy!" she said. "I want to thank everyone who voted for me!" They cheered enthusiastically as she lifted the winner's trophy.

Write three pieces of text – one in the first, one in the second and one in the third person.

LOOK FOR EXAMPLES IN BOOKS TO HELP YOU.

First person

_____

_____

_____

_____

Second person

_____

_____

_____

_____

Third person

_____

_____

_____

_____

get it?

There are two main types of writing. **Fiction** is not true; it is made up by the story-teller. **Non-fiction** is true; it is writing based on facts and real events.

writing stories (fiction)

When you write a story the first thing you need to decide on is where (and when) the action takes place – this is called the **setting**.

Writers often set their stories in places that are familiar to them, for example school, home, neighbourhood, workplace or somewhere they went on holiday.

Possible settings:

new school	raging river	remote rainforest
busy airport	noisy campsite	space station

Choose one of these settings and write notes on the mind-map below about the things you can see, hear, touch, taste or smell.

USE A SEPARATE PIECE OF PAPER IF YOU NEED MORE SPACE TO WRITE.

DECIDE WHETHER THE SETTING IS IN THE *PAST*, *PRESENT* OR *FUTURE*.

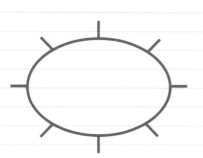

Characters are essential to tell the story.

Any characters you invent should have a clear purpose in the story and a distinct personality. They might be unusual in some way, eg in the way they dress or speak.

Match the following characters to the settings in the box above.
There are no right or wrong answers.

Polly Phonic – friendly, talkative	**Venus Strange** – clever, mysterious
Miss McEvil – controlling, ambitious	**Gazza Green** – loud, outdoorsy-type
Ace Bravado – dare-devil, adventure seeker	**Leif Biome** – wacky, curious nature

Now choose one of these characters and invent others to match your chosen setting.
Make up names and character descriptions. Use a separate piece of paper for this work.

All stories must have a **plot** or **theme** – this is what the story is about and what the characters do.

Here are some popular story ideas:

Possible plots:

good versus evil	a misunderstanding	a comedy
something is lost or stolen	journey of discovery	friendship theme

Choose a plot to match your setting and characters.

Write a story plan in five paragraphs:

Beginning – introduce your setting and characters

_____

_____

Build up – things start to happen and the plot develops

_____

_____

Crisis – a series of things go wrong, leading to a crisis

_____

_____

Solution – the characters manage to sort out the problem

_____

_____

Ending – the characters reflect on what has happened or changed

_____

_____

Now you are ready to write out your story in full!
Use a separate piece of paper for this.

stick a reward sticker here!

writing non-fiction

Reports, recounts, instructions and discussions are examples of **non-fiction** writing.

Reports – writing about the facts known on a given topic. Use specialist vocabulary and define the terms used. Use a formal style in present tense. Illustrate with diagrams or pictures.

Recounts – writing about an event you have witnessed or an experience you have had. Use pronouns: I, we, he, she, they. Write in the past tense using powerful verbs. Use time connectives, for example then, when, later, next, eventually.

Instructions – writing about how to do something. Include lists of materials needed. Write a clear sequence of steps. Use verbs, for example cut, mix, stir, place. Use time connectives and pronouns such as you and your.

Discussions – writing about a topic to provide a balanced viewpoint or discussion. Write the points 'for' and 'against', using evidence to back up the argument. Use present tense and emotional language to engage with the reader. Reach a conclusion at the end.

Read the following report text:

Fast Cats

The cheetah is the fastest land animal. Cheetahs can reach speeds of up to 70 miles per hour (113 kph). They can accelerate faster than the average car: 0 to 60 miles per hour in only 3 seconds!

Their long legs and athletic bodies are built for fast acceleration. Wildebeest, their prey, are fast too but they are slower to accelerate. The cheetah, however, can't maintain this speed over long distances so sometimes the wildebeest manage to outrun them.

Larger cats such as leopards and tigers are slower because their bulkier bodies have to use more muscle and energy to propel them forwards. They can reach up to 35-40 miles per hour in short bursts.

Domestic cats can run up to 30 miles per hour. They have lost some of their speed because they no longer need to chase their dinner!

Now answer these questions in complete sentences:

1. What makes the cheetah so fast?

_____

_____

2. Is the cheetah faster than the fastest car?

_____

_____

3. How does the wildebeest manage to outrun the cheetah?

_____

_____

4. What is the opposite of a domestic cat?

_____

_____

5. What tense (past, present or future) is the text written in?

_____

_____

stick a
reward
sticker
here!

a discussion

Read the following discussion text:

Do dogs make good pets?

People have kept dogs as pets for hundreds of years. Dogs can be easily house-trained to live in our homes. They form loyal and protective bonds with their owners and for older people who live alone, a dog can provide companionship. Studies have shown that dog owners tend to be happier and healthier because the daily walks they give their dogs have health benefits for them also.

However, owning a dog comes with responsibilities. Dogs need feeding, exercising, love and affection, and someone to look after them when their owners go on holiday. One of the biggest complaints against dog ownership is dog-fouling. Despite fines of up to £1,000 there are still some irresponsible owners who do not clean up after their pets.

Dogs make good pets and they bring great rewards for many people but they bring responsibilities too which should not be forgotten. Dogs are not like toys given at Christmas that can be thrown away when we tire of them – a dog is for life.

get it?

The first paragraph outlines arguments 'for', the second paragraph outlines arguments 'against' and the final paragraph gives a conclusion.

Write a similar balanced argument: Do cats make good pets?* Use a separate piece of paper for this.

*Or any other animal you choose.

a recount

Read the following recount:

When I arrived home at 7 pm, I immediately knew something was wrong. The first thing I noticed was the light through the upstairs window when I knew I hadn't left it on. Then I saw that the front door was wide open! I stepped nervously into the hallway and everything looked okay. Next, I went into the living room and to my dismay I saw that some squatters had moved in! Then I called the police.

Now answer these questions in complete sentences:

1. What time connectives have been used in the text? List them below.

_____

2. What tense (past, present or future) is the text written in? Examine the verbs to find out.

_____

3. Is the text written in the first, second or third person? Explain your answer.

_____

Write a recount of a past event or experience that you can remember.
Use extra paper if needed.

_____

_____

_____

_____

_____

writing formal letters

stick a reward sticker here!

WRITE YOUR ADDRESS HERE:

THE RECIPIENT'S ADDRESS IS WRITTEN HERE:

_____

_____

_____

The Manager
Pizza Palace
Garlic Street
Doughton
ET7 UP1

WRITE THE DATE HERE:

WRITE A FORMAL LETTER TO COMPLAIN ABOUT THE LACK OF TOPPINGS ON A PIZZA YOU BOUGHT FROM A FAST FOOD RESTAURANT. MAKE IT CLEAR WHY YOU ARE WRITING THIS LETTER, E.G. DO YOU WANT A REFUND?

_____

Dear Sir/Madam,

_____

_____

_____

_____

_____

Yours faithfully,

_____

WRITE YOUR SIGNATURE HERE:

get it?

If you know the name of the person you are addressing, you end with 'Yours sincerely'.

answers

know your nouns
1. I hurt my knee.
2. The paint is still wet.
3. Don't touch the exhibits!
4. Red is my favourite colour.
5. Can I have a biscuit?
6. Let's go for a walk.

1. a pod of dolphins
2. a shoal of fish
3. a colony of ants
4. a crowd of people
5. a galaxy of stars
6. a fleet of ships
7. a clutch of eggs
8. a litter of puppies

perfect your pronouns
1. The reds beat the blues. They won by two points.
2. Jack loved the film when he saw it.
3. Bella is in my class. Do you know her?
4. Our neighbours are friendly when you get to know them.

1. The ice cream belongs to Amy. It's hers.
2. The snake belongs to us. It's ours.
3. The hat belongs to you. It's yours.
4. The car belongs to them. It's theirs.

adding adjectives
1. The <u>clever</u> detective caught the <u>notorious</u> thief.
2. <u>Spectacular</u> fireworks lit up the <u>dark</u> sky.
3. A <u>big, hairy</u> spider sat beside the <u>little</u> boy.

comparing adjectives
er	est
bigger	biggest
louder	loudest
funnier	funniest
healthier	healthiest

1. The triceratops was <u>heavier</u> than two elephants.
2. Energy-saving bulbs last <u>longer</u> than ordinary bulbs.
3. Wind energy is <u>greener</u> than oil.
4. Vegetables are <u>healthier</u> than cakes.
5. Of all the jellyfish, the box jellyfish is the <u>most deadly</u>.

verbs and adverbs
Here are some possible answers:
1. He looked fiercely at his opponent.
2. They spoke quietly on the phone.
3. She sang softly into the microphone.
4. The wind blew gently.
5. The volcano erupted violently.

playing with words
1. a ray of sunshine
2. a snake in the grass
3. a fly in the ointment
4. a night owl

1. Other people's lives always seem better than our own.
2. You risk losing everything if you put all your resources in one thing.
3. Two people might be able to solve a problem that one person cannot.
4. It is better to do something late than not at all.
5. Something can look flashy but not be valuable.

how to use apostrophes
1. the teacher's desk
2. Mum's purse
3. the artist's studio
4. the cat's whiskers

1. the girls' dog
2. the family's car
3. the players' changing room
4. the people's jobs
5. the babies' toys

1. We can't go yet.
2. She didn't like the taste.
3. The dog doesn't bite.
4. The car won't start.
5. It's not fair! / It isn't fair!

speech!

> "I think Dig is sick," said Tom. "He won't eat his dinner."
> "Perhaps he's not hungry," replied Tom's mum.
> "But he's *always* hungry!" said Tom. "And it's his favourite: marinated chicken chunks in juicy jelly."

The position of the exclamation marks can vary depending on which words you want to emphasise. Here is one possibility:

> "Mum!" shouted Tom.
> "Now what?" said Tom's mum.
> "I know why Dig won't eat his dinner," said Tom.
> "It's a new recipe. They've added vegetables! You know he hates vegetables!"

clauses and conjunctions

Here are some examples:
1. Dig didn't eat his dinner so Kit ate it instead.
2. Dig and Kit were friends but they were rivals too.
3. Tom was worried when Dig didn't eat.
4. Mum wasn't paying attention because she was busy.

1. I put the dog on the lead <u>and</u> we went out for a walk.
2. It felt cold <u>although</u> it was sunny.
3. We played in the park <u>until</u> it was dark.
4. Mum was cross <u>when</u> I got home late.
5. I missed my programme <u>because</u> it came on earlier than usual.

1. I missed the last five minutes of the film. <u>Consequently</u>, I don't know how it ended!
2. I can come to your house. <u>However</u>, I can't stay for long.
3. Firstly, you mix the butter and the sugar. <u>Next</u>, you add the egg.
4. Dad did the shopping. <u>Meanwhile</u>, Mum was at work.
5. Do your homework now. <u>Later</u>, you can go swimming.

prefix

1. aquarium
   aquatic
   aquamarine

2. vivisect
   vivacious
   vivid

3. geometry
   geology
   geography

4. biography
   bionic
   biological

5. octopus
   octagon
   octave

6. supermarket
   supersonic
   superstore

suffix

1. instructor
2. actor
3. conductor

4. hopeless
5. sleepless
6. restless

7. excitement
8. movement
9. agreement

10. immediately
11. suddenly
12. extremely

1. spiced
2. caring
3. later
4. biggest
5. swimming
6. stopped

plural suffixes

wishes
kisses
boxes
lunches
buses

cities
ponies
memories
dictionaries

rhymes and alliteration

1. shoes and news
2. chomps and chases, dog and Dig
3. shoes, chews, news, mews, blues, bruise, fuse, whose, cruise, hues, views. Did you think of any more?

different kinds of writing

Somehow <u>I</u> knew that today was going to be special, even though it started off like every other day – <u>I</u> was going to be late for school again!

To make chocolate brownies <u>you</u> need: flour, cocoa powder, eggs, butter and milk. But first, <u>you</u> need to find an adult or parent to help <u>you</u>!

"I'm so happy!" <u>she</u> said. "I want to thank everyone who voted for me!" <u>They</u> cheered enthusiastically as <u>she</u> lifted the winner's trophy.

fast cats

1. The cheetah is fast because it has long legs and an athletic body.
2. The cheetah is faster than the average car.
3. The wildebeest can outrun the cheetah because it can maintain its speed over longer distances.
4. A wild cat is the opposite of a domestic cat.
5. The text is written in present tense.

a recount

<u>When</u> I arrived home at 7 pm, I <u>immediately</u> knew something was wrong. The <u>first</u> thing I noticed was the light through the upstairs window when I knew I hadn't left it on. <u>Then</u> I saw that the front door was wide open! I stepped nervously into the hallway and everything looked okay. <u>Next</u>, I went into the living room and to my dismay I saw that some squatters had moved in! <u>Then</u> I called the police.

1. The following time connectives are used: 'when', 'immediately', 'first', 'then' and 'next'.
2. The text is written in the past tense.
3. The text is written in the first person because the pronouns 'I' and 'my' are used.